Lines Upon the Water

A Collection of Original Songs
by Sheila Douglas

illustrations by Drea Peters

OSSIAN

Illustrated by Drea Peters
Cover photograph by The Scottish Highland Photo Library
Photo of Sheila on back cover by Les MacGowan, Scone.
Design, Text/Music typesetting and Layout by Colin Douglas

Printed by Colour Books, Dublin

● A cassette tape with 17 songs from this book,
   sung by Sheila is also available:
   Lines Upon the Water Ossian OSS 99

Ossian Publications
Publishers & Distributors of Irish, Scottish & General Music
in Print, Sound and Vision.
For our complete catalogue, send us your name and address
with an (international) postal reply coupon

Ossian Publications
P.O.Box 84, Cork, Ireland
E-Mail: ossian@iol.ie
Web: www.ossian.ie

Ossian OMB 104
ISBN 1 946005 89 3

Lines Upon The Water

Contents

3. Comedy and Satire

4. Real Life and History

5. Glossary

Foreword

At long last, the Sheila Douglas Songbook! It is a great pleasure, as well as an honour, to commend it to you. Sheila has made such a contribution to the traditional arts in Scotland as collector, storyteller, singer, organiser and language activist that her considerable skill as a makar is sometimes in danger of being overlooked.

Part of that long and honourable line of balladeers whose work was a commentary on the happenings of their day, Sheila allies a facility for words, in both Scots and English, with a good ear for a fitting tune. Her ability to fashion a television news item into a song which is not only eminently singable but thought provoking too is well exemplified by the song which gives this book its title. The tale of an errant trawlerman having his gear confiscated is turned into an ironic reflection on the ephemeral nature of human concerns. A far-sighted view of the consequences of oil industry money on Scottish rural communities inspired the much sung and recorded *Men o the North*.

Sheila's subject matter ranges far and wide through love and friendship, history and politics, and her gifts as a comic songwriter – a much more difficult art than it looks – have delighted us for years. The misadventures of the Auchentoshan Fire Brigade, the fate of the Comrie Bull, and the sexual symbolism of a variety of musical instruments have all inspired comic classics. Every time I find myself toying with the idea of taking more exercise, going on a diet, or joining a health club, the words of Sheila's *Keep Fit Song* come into my head and I sensibly sit down and have a cream bun!

It is possibly, though, as a chronicler of tragedy that Sheila excels most. Whether it be the disastrous fire at Michael Colliery, the horror of Aberfan, or the outrage of Dunblane, her compassionate but unsentimental voice finds the right words and the appropriate melody to carry them.

Sheila's songs deserve to be more widely known and sung, and this book will be a treasure trove for singers for years to come.

Sheena Wellington

Acknowledgements

Grateful thanks are due to the following people for their contribution to the publishing of this book :–

Sheena Wellington for providing the *Foreword*; to my elder son Colin for all his hard work in transcribing the music of all the songs and the design and typesetting of the text; and finally to Christina Fleming for giving up what little free time she had in a busy work schedule to help check over the proofs.

Sheila M. Douglas

This collection of original songs is dedicated to the memory of the late Arthur Argo of Aberdeen, who not only worked unceasingly to preserve Scottish folk traditions, but also encouraged new songwriting talent, including myself, to add our own contributions to Scotland's rich heritage.

1. Love and Friendship

Mothers all over the world have had problems getting their children to go to sleep at one time or other. Perhaps the most traditional methods of achieving this is to read them a favourite story or sing them a lullaby. This is a lullaby written for my own children in the early 1960s, using the old French-derived cradling croon.

✳ ✳ ✳ ✳ ✳ ✳ ✳ ✳ ✳ ✳ ✳

Balulaloo

Gently

Soft - ly croons the cu - shie doo In the gloa - min

dim an blue. Nicht comes cree - pin by the cairn

Chorus

Bring - in dreams tae my— wee bairn. Ba - lu - la - loo,

ba - lu - la - lay, Sleep wee lamb till blink o day.

Ba - lu - la - loo, ba - lu - la - loo, The

hill - tap moon will watch owre you.

2. Dusk is on the shadowy corn,
   Whaup an mavis sleep till morn,
   Ilka beastie seeks its den,
   Houlets cry fae yonder glen.
Chorus: *Balulaloo, balulalay,*
   Sleep wee lamb till blink o day,
   Balulaloo, balulaloo,
   The hilltap moon will watch owre you.

3. Firelicht dances on the waa,
   Doun the veils o darkness faa,
   By the door's the rowan tree
   That keeps the hoose o warlocks free.
Chorus: *Balulaloo, balulalay, ... etc.*

4. Bairnie rest an close your eyes,
   Dinna wake me wi your cries,
   By your cradle I am here,
   Ghaists nor ghoulies need ye fear.
Chorus: *Balulaloo, balulalay, ... etc.*

During our time as students at Glasgow University in the 1950s, my husband Andrew and I were exposed to many of the different cultures of the world thanks to the International Club. We thoroughly enjoyed mixing with the overseas students who frequented the many gatherings, and it has instilled us both with a respect for other cultures. Racism is something that has always been repugnant to me, and this song tries to say why.

✳ ✳ ✳ ✳ ✳ ✳ ✳ ✳ ✳ ✳ ✳ ✳

Black and White

And will you wed a stran-ger From a far off fo-reign land? And will you touch his black, black skin with the white-ness of your hand?

Chorus

Can't you see, can't you see, mo-ther, oh mo-ther, Can't you see he's a man Just like a-ny o-ther?

2. "And will you cook his foreign food
   And go his foreign way?
   And will he lie down by your side
   At the closing of the day?"
   "Can't you see, can't you see,
   Mother, oh mother,
   Can't you see he's a man
   Just like any other?"

3. "And will he be the father
   Of the children that you bear?
   And will you mind as you walk by
   If people stop and stare?"
   "Can't they see, can't they see,
   Mother, oh mother,
   I'm a woman, he's a man,
   Just like any other?"

4. "Have you quite forgotten
   All the lessons you have learned,
   That black is black and white is white
   And completely different?"
   "Lies, all lies, lies, all lies,
   Mother, oh mother,
   Black and white are human beings
   Just like one another!"

Scotland's national bard, Robert Burns is well known for having an eye for the lasses, and there were many lasses who attracted his eye throughout his life. But the one he fell for and, in the end, married was Jean Armour. This song tries to imagine what her feelings must have been for her complex "ploughman poet".

✳ ✳ ✳ ✳ ✳ ✳ ✳ ✳ ✳ ✳ ✳

Jean Armour's Song

When dark - ness blins___ the eye o day, A - cross the
hill I'll take my way. An laigh a - low___ the
rig I'll___ stray, Tae meet an greet___ my bon - nie___ love.

2.   Dark his eye an saft his tongue,
       Aa the sweetest sangs he's sung,
       An my very hert he's wrung
       Wi his tender words o love.

3.   Fortune sparesna owre much time,
       Yet I'll love him in my prime.
       Tae his tune I'll fit my rhyme
       An aye I'll mind his vows o love

4. An tho my faither isnae kind,
    His stern rebukes I winna mind.
    But tho I'm fain, my love's no blind:
    I ken that Rab's a lad tae rove.

5. But let him rove or stay at hame,
    Whate'er he'll do I'll think nae shame,
    An I'll love him jist the same
    For he's my ane an only love.

My husband and I have been going to folk festivals for thirty years and during that time we have met and made friends with many fine people and we have shared times of great happiness and tragedy together. One of the wisest people I have ever met was Betsy Whyte. Sadly, she died when we were all staying at Duncan Williamson's house over the weekend of Auchtermuchty Festival in 1990. This song, written to the tune of *Tatties and Herrin*, is my tribute to her.

❊ ❊ ❊ ❊ ❊ ❊ ❊ ❊ ❊ ❊ ❊ ❊

Rowans & Honey

O— Bet - sy, your words were the wis - est of aa. Ye aye spoke wi wis - dom what - e'er micht be - faa, Wi plen - ty o love tho there was - nae much mo - ney, Your life was a mix - ture o row - ans and ho - ney.

Chorus

Row-ans and ho - ney, row - ans and ho-ney, Your life was a mix - ture o row - ans and ho - ney.

2. The stories ye told were o wonders and magic,
   They threaded their way thro the comic and tragic.
   We loved them all, baith the sad and the funny
   For they taught that in life there's baith rowans and honey.
Chorus: *Rowans and honey, rowans and honey,*
   They taught that in life there's baith rowans and honey.

3. When sorrow and daith mak us grumble and glower,
   Their taste like the rowan is bitter and sour.
   But then when oor days are aa joyfu and sunny,
   Oor pleisure is sweet like the taste o the honey.
Chorus: *Rowans and honey, rowans and honey,*
   Oor pleisure is sweet like the taste o the honey.

4. Ye traivelt the country when ye were a bairn
   An mony hard lessons o life ye'd tae learn.
   But the truth o it aa ye kent better than ony,
   Baith nakins and hantle share rowans and honey.
Chorus: *Rowans and honey, rowans and honey,*
   Baith nakins and hantle share rowans and honey.

There are a couple of traveller's cant words in the fourth verse which the uninitiated might not know. *Nakins* means travellers, and *hantle* means settled people.

My songwriting has spanned the entire period of the Folk Revival in Scotland, and I have been influenced by many of its luminaries. This is a love song written for my husband Andrew in the early days of the Revival, when I was strongly influenced by Ewan McColl.

✳ ✳ ✳ ✳ ✳ ✳ ✳ ✳ ✳ ✳ ✳

Look At Me, My Love

O look_____ at me, my love, And say you will ne - ver go. Look_____ at me, my love, In your eyes the truth will show. Sweet lips may lie, Sweet words fly off on the wind and die, But look_____ at me, my love, And all your_____ heart I'll know.

2. In your eyes, my love, lies the blue eternal sea,
   In it lies, my love, what the future holds for me:
   Storms or calms,
   A safe and happy haven in your arms.
   Were we wise, my love, how easy love would be.

3. Here we stand, my love, upon the quiet shore,
   Safe on land, my love, tho far-off billows roar.
   Doubtless salt tears
   Will rive our cheeks as we go down the years,
   But take my hand, my love, and you'll be alone no more.

Over the last thirty years of the Revival, festivals have proliferated all over Scotland from Shetland to Newcastleton; many of them being run by, or affiliated to the Traditional Music and Song Association, who run competitions in everything from traditional singing and storytelling to fiddle and accordion playing and original composition. This song was written for a songwriting competition run by the Angus Branch for it's festival in Kirriemuir. It was to be linked to two sets of initials carved into an old door lintel, believed to be those of the couple who had occupied the house, according to a romantic old custom. Kirriemuir used to be a busy textile town. The tune is traditional.

✳ ✳ ✳ ✳ ✳ ✳ ✳ ✳ ✳ ✳ ✳ ✳

The Kirrie Wabster

When first I met my sweet——hairt it was doon by Bel-ly's—— Brae, He smiled on me sae kind——-ly an con-voyed me on my way. And mo-ny a time he took me—— in Glen-is-la—— for tae stray. When the bir-ken trees bloomed bon-nie—— in the—— sim-mer—— O.

2. He was a wabster laddie an he workit at the loom;
   He telt me that my bonnie face was like a rose in bloom.
   An aften in the gloamin he wad tak me tae the broom,
   When the mune abune the Westmuir Lan wad glimmer O.

3. He coortit me a sax-month lang an gied tae me a ring,
   An wi't he hecht tae wad me jist as sune as it was Spring.
   An noo we bide contentit like ony queen or king
   Wi oor names abune the lintel in the timmer O.

4. So come aa ye servant lassies fae Kirrie an aroon;
   Ne'er be sweirt tae tak a wabster laddie fae the toon.
   He'll aye be true an ye will never want for coat or goon,
   An he will never lack a speedy spinner O.

The four seasons of the year – Spring, Summer, Autumn and Winter – have a direct influence on all our lives. Many poets and songsmiths have observed the various moods of the seasons and this is my attempt to express the sadder mood of Autumn, when natural things begin to die off with the final passing of the summer and the oncoming winter just around the corner.

✳ ✳ ✳ ✳ ✳ ✳ ✳ ✳ ✳ ✳ ✳ ✳

Autumn Song

The   birds they   are lea—— vin   the   dead leaves   are fal—— lin   A -

bove the   cold roof—— tops   the   wild   geese   are cal—— lin   The

Au - tumn   is   here   an   the   old   year   is   dy—— in,   An

if   I   knew   how——   wi   the   birds   I'd   be   fly—— in.

2. The summer is gone an the bright sun-burned faces
   An the flowers are all withered from the bare woodland places.
   There's mist on the hill an a frost in the mornin
   An a wind whose cold breath holds a wintery warnin.

3. Well I just can't stay here an there's nowhere to run to,
   I think I must die, in fact, I've begun to.
   Now the sun an the moon no longer light the sky's cover,
   Since I said goodbye to the arms of my lover.

4. The birds they are leaving, the blown branches are bendin,
   An the life an the love of the year have an endin.
   Soon the ground will be hard an the daylight soon dyin,
   An if I knew how, wi the birds I'd be flyin.

Ceilidhing is one of life's great pleasures as far as I am concerned. Sadly, most of the present day generation seem to have discarded this traditional way of making your own entertainment, preferring to have it served up to them on a plate in the form of television programmes and computer games. This song is a memory of the days in the 1960s and 70s when my family and I used to go up to Dave Goulder's hostel at Glen Cottage in Wester Ross, to enjoy the peace and quiet after a hectic school term, sing late into the night and see the changing seasons pass through the glen.

✳ ✳ ✳ ✳ ✳ ✳ ✳ ✳ ✳ ✳ ✳

· **The Torridon Lilt**

With a gentle lilt

Tow' - ring rocks · wind shaped and sun har———— dened,

Path - less slopes of heath - er and scree, Lone and far in the

sky of the north——·—— land, Still I hear you call - ing to me.

2. Over the road I'll go to Glen Docherty
   Where in the distance lies Loch Maree,
   Then by Kinlochewe to the glen winding softly,
   Where high on Ben Eighe the stag wanders free.

3. When the crest of Liathach is crowned with the snowdrift
   And from the high corries the eagle looks down,
   There's mist upon the slopes of Ben Alligin,
   And winter sun finds the bracken turned brown.

4. Summer steps lightly across the grey Coulin
   And follows the glen road down to Shieldaig.
   There in the track of the hare or the moorhen,
   She wanders contented by lochside or craig.

5. If your steps should lead to Torridon,
   You will echo the lilt of my song.
   And tho elsewhere your footsteps are hurried on,
   Memories of it will linger for long.

6. Far away from cities and motorways,
   Rich men's mansions and factory walls,
   May Torridon always be there to bring hearts-ease
   Among the peaks and high waterfalls.

The folk music scene is full of singers who have been influenced by others. As I have mentioned earlier, one of my influences on my songwriting in the early 1960s was Ewan McColl. At the risk of embarrassing him, I have to confess that this song was written to my favourite singer at that time, Archie Fisher, who sang his songs, and still does, in a simple, unpretentious manner that shows respect and feeling for the lyrics.

❋ ❋ ❋ ❋ ❋ ❋ ❋ ❋ ❋ ❋ ❋

Fine Singing Laddie

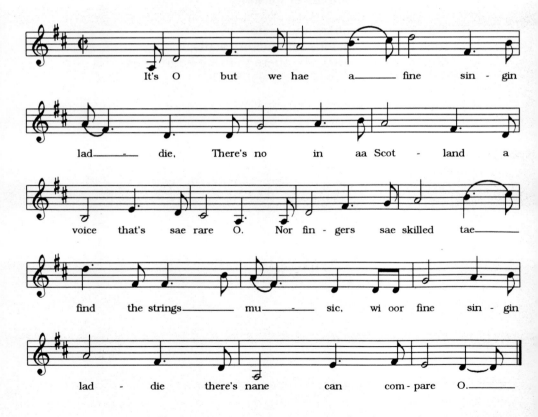

2. The auld sangs, the great sangs, that move the hert deeply,
   There's nane that can sing them sae sweetly as he O.
   An the tender re-tellin o love an sad pairtin,
   He gies the fond note that brings tears tae the ee O.

3. There's no a guid sang but oor braw laddie kens it,
   An weel loes he ballads baith bawdy an fey O.
   An verses that lauch owre oor ain mortal failins
   That spile oor gran schemes an lead us agley O.

4. It's gratefu we are tae oor fine singin laddie,
   Wha's voice sae delichts us wi pleisure tae hear O.
   His gift is mair worth than the pearls fun on Tayside,
   Tae aa oor blithe herts he's a treasure sae dear O.

During my days at Glasgow University, I crossed the Clyde on the Renfrew Ferry each day, so the river does hold many memories for me. I tried this song as an experiment to see if *Sweet Thames Flow Softly* by Ewan McColl could be transferred northward. The Clyde is such a beautiful river with its historic city surroundings and its island-studded firth.

✳ ✳ ✳ ✳ ✳ ✳ ✳ ✳ ✳ ✳ ✳

Sweet Clyde Flow Softly

I met my lass by John Brown's yard, A-neath the big crane's
shad-die. I took her hame tae Par-tick Cross And swore I'd be her
lad-die. Aa the lights u-pon the ri-ver shi-nin on the
wa-ter-side For a neck-lace I would give her, Sweet Clyde flow
soft-ly. Fer-ried ow-re tae Go-van Cross, Flow sweet ri-ver flow,
Stars in-to her lap I'd toss, Sweet Clyde flow soft-ly.

2. We held hands on the Broomielaw and went aboard a steamer,
    We set aff for the Kyles o Bute when simmer was a dreamer.
    Aa the islands on the river; Arran blue and Cumbrae green,
    For a gairden I wad give her (sweet Clyde, flow softly).
    Mountain mist tae be her shawl (flow, sweet river, flow),
    And raindrops sparkling as they fall (sweet Clyde, flow softly).

3. I tuik her in a warm embrace as we sailed by Dumbarton,
    While heather on the Gourock hills glowed like some ancient tartan.
    Aa the seabirds on the river, swooping white abune the spray,
    For dancin pairtners I wad give her (sweet Clyde, flow softly).
    Dance upon the dark green waves (flow, sweet river, flow),
    Dance thro Arran's rocky caves (sweet Clyde, flow softly).

4. We lay as yin on Brodick sands when munelicht glinted bonnie,
    Wi herts entwined for evermair – o care we hadnae ony.
    Aa the fishes in the river, aa the waves upon the sea,
    For her fortune I wad give her (sweet Clyde, flow softly).
    Shinin chuckies white an green (flow, sweet river, flow),
    Croon, my love, my river queen (sweet Clyde, flow softly).

The Folk Revival rapidly gathered pace through the 1960s and 1970s and spread across the world. Folk clubs sprang up everywhere across Scotland, and I had the pleasure of running Perth Folk Club for six years. This is my tribute to one of the great international troubadours in the Revival, Alex Campbell, who made more than one appearance in Perth. I wonder if this rings any bells with anybody who remembers hearing him perform?

✳ ✳ ✳ ✳ ✳ ✳ ✳ ✳ ✳ ✳ ✳

A Toast to Alex Campbell

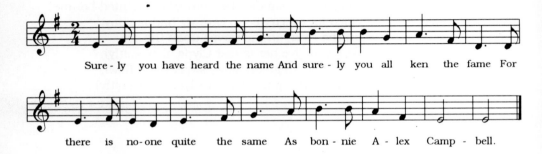

Sure - ly you have heard the name And sure - ly you all ken the fame For

there is no-one quite the same As bon - nie A - lex Camp - bell.

2. He had sung baith far and wide
   Frae Mississippi tae the Clyde;
   His greatness canna be denied,
   We're prood o Alex Campbell.

3. When he picks his big guitar
   And lifts his voice tae droon the bar,
   It's then we ken we hae a star
   In bonnie Alex Campbell

4. He's always fu o jokes and chaff
   He likes a whisky and a half,
   The lassies loe his dirty laugh:
   He's a terror, Alex Campbell!

5. When in Paris he hauds sway:
   He's caaed Le Cowboy Écossais.
   And there he's busked on mony a day,
   Ce méchant, Alex Campbell.

6. But it gets tiring on the road,
   He seldom sees his own abode,
   And life can be a weary load
   When you're bonnie Alex Campbell.

7. Lang may he sing the world's best sangs,
   And talk o righting human wrangs,
   An peace for which the haill warld langs:
   Here's a toast tae Alex Campbell.

Out of all the many friends my husband and I have made over the last thirty years, among the most valued have been found among the Perthshire travelling community. Willie MacPhee is the last of the traveller tinsmiths; a piper, storyteller and singer, whom I am proud to call friend. This song, written to a traditional tune, is his life story as he told it to me while I was working towards my doctorate on the storytelling traditions of the Perthshire travellers. Now living quietly on a travellers' caravan site on the outskirts of Perth, he was harrassed for years by the law which prevents travellers from camping in the many places where it was once traditional.

❋ ❋ ❋ ❋ ❋ ❋ ❋ ❋ ❋ ❋ ❋ ❋

Willie MacPhee's Song

It was in nine-teen ten that I first saw day - licht In a
hoose wi a roof an a fire——side bricht. My
mi - ther an fai - ther warked hard on the fairm, An they
did aa they cuid for tae keep me frae hairm.

2. Then when the crops were aa planted an hoed,
   My Dad took the notion tae gang on the road.
   We traivelt thro Scotland an Ireland as well,
   An that was my schuilin the truth for tae tell.

3. On the road, a guid livin's no easily made,
   Sae I became maister o mony a trade:
   Tinsmithin an pipin an fairmwark tae,
   An ony ither job that I fun for tae dae.

4. I'm a dab haun at makin the baskets an creels
   An playin pipe mairches an strathspeys an reels.
   I can mend an auld engine or cure a lame horse,
   An I like best tae camp amang heather an gorse.

5. But times aye get harder an when the wark's dune,
   The polis arrive an they're movin us on.
   Oh ye cannae camp here an ye cannae camp there –
   Sune the wan place that's left'll be up in the air.

6. Sae I'll tak a rocket an gang tae the mune,
   I'll fin a guid campsite an never come doon.
   When you hear my pipes playin clear, lood an high,
   Ye'll ken Willie MacPhee's in his hame in the sky.

When this song was written, conflicts were going on in Vietnam and we also had the Cold War, where the powers that be were influenced by a spirit of mistrust. If we look to the world of nature, there is always hope for the future in growing things and in the cycle of the seasons.

✻ ✻ ✻ ✻ ✻ ✻ ✻ ✻ ✻ ✻

Hope

Freely

Fields of snow, you're bleak as lone - li - ness;——— You lie as dead with-out the sun's ca-ress.——— When it shone. Life went on with eve - ry hour de - ligh - ting in its pride,——— Then it died and all the ro - ses of the sum - mer were gone.

2. Fields of snow, so desolate and bare
   You teach my heart never to despair,
   For I know
   When the snow
   Melts with the coming of the Spring,
   Birds will sing
   And all the roses of the summer will grow.

2. Tragedy and Sadness

Tragedies can take many forms. When something awful happens and it results in a loss of life, we all feel a sense of tragedy. The war in Bosnia was equally tragic for those who have escaped with their own lives, but have nevertheless been adversely affected by it in some way. I wrote this song while the war was still raging after reading in the paper that mental hospitals in Sarajevo were having to release their patients because they no longer had the resources to look after them properly. I tried to imagine how they would view the mad world they found outside. The whole situation seemed to reflect the insanity of war.

✳ ✳ ✳ ✳ ✳ ✳ ✳ ✳ ✳ ✳ ✳ ✳

The Madmen in the Streets

When the mad - men are set free on the streets of Sa - ra - je - vo, Will they un - der-stand the dif - fer-ence be - tween The____ hell that's in their heads and the hell that's all____ a- round them. Or will they feel it's where they've al - ways been?

Chorus

Al - ways been. Al - ways been.____ Or will they feel it's where they've al - ways been?

2. When their bodies meet the bullets that are fired by their brothers,
   Will they cry against the injustice and the shame?
   And will they understand, as they thole the living nightmare,
   Not just themselves but the world has gone insane?
Chorus: *Gone insane, gone insane!*
   Not just themselves but the world has gone insane!

3. In the streets of Sarajevo, there are wives and mothers mourning
   For death of husbands, slaughter of their sons.
   But they don't fear the madmen that wander through the alleys:
   They only fear the madmen carrying guns.
Chorus: *Carrying guns, carrying guns,*
   They only fear the madmen carrying guns.

The close-knit coastal communities around Scotland's coastline have always been particularly close to tragedy. The North Sea and the North Atlantic can be among the world's most inhospitable environments in which to work, and fishermen risk their lives to earn the money they bring home in order to clothe and feed their families. Among the bravest working in this environment are our liveboat crews. The worst aspect of the loss of the Longhope lifeboat in the late 1960s was the knowledge that it need not have happened at all.

✳ ✳ ✳ ✳ ✳ ✳ ✳ ✳ ✳ ✳ ✳ ✳

The Longhope Lifeboat

With Pathos

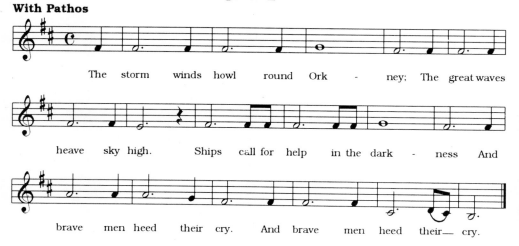

The storm winds howl round Ork - ney; The great waves heave sky high. Ships call for help in the dark - ness And brave men heed their cry. And brave men heed their— cry.

2. Running down to the boat shed
    Then out on the wild, wild sea,
    There goes the Longhope lifeboat
    Doomed to eternity.

3. Far on the gale-lashed ocean,
    Lost in that night of death,
    The Longhope heroes strove onward
    Till the sea took life and breath.

4. There in the light of morning
   An upturned boat was seen,
   With seven corpses in the wheelhouse
   Where eight fine men had been.

5. Widows are weeping in Orkney,
   Mothers and sisters cry
   For the men of the Longhope lifeboat
   Who sailed in the storm to die.

6. There's a question still unanswered
   Of a ship that should not have left port,
   For 'twas she who sent out the signal
   When the fuel in her bunkers ran short.

7. Whatever may be the answer,
   It's no comfort to those who remain
   Lamenting the Longhope heroes
   Who'll ne'er put to sea again.

This song is very much a tribute to the travelling people who bear the injustice of continually being moved off land by the police at the request of uncaring landowners who mistakenly see the travellers as a burden to them. It was written for Winged Horse's stage production of Ann Downie's adaptation of Betsy Whyte's book *The Yellow on the Broom*. This book tells the story of Betsy's childhood as a Perthshire traveller and gives us an insight of the time when travellers were a valuable asset to the landowner in the form of cheap manual labour on the farms.

✳ ✳ ✳ ✳ ✳ ✳ ✳ ✳ ✳ ✳ ✳

Moving On

Nae— land tae caa oor ain And the haill warld tae wan-der——— And we're

aye and for- ev- er mo- vin on Tae——— tramp the wea - ry

road In the rain, sun and thun- der,——— Like a bur - nie by the

Chorus

road- side rin- nin on. Mo - vin on, we're aye mo - vin on. Hitch the

pow - ny tae the yoke, we're mo - vin on. Mo - vin on, we're

aye   mo - vin   on.   Nae mair meal in - tae   the poke, we're mo - vin on.

    2. We ask nae mair tae eat but oor tatties and oor brochan
       And we're aye and forever movin on.
       We're mony a day sair trachled and mony a nicht forfochen,
       Like a tree that the storm has blawn upon.
Chorus: *Movin on, we're aye movin on.*
           Hitch the powny tae the yoke, we're movin on.
           Movin on, we're aye movin on.
           Nae mair meal intae the poke, we're movin on.

    3. We'll work for honest wages, we'll mak baskets and sell them,
       And we're aye and forever movin on.
       But what can ye dae when your face isnae welcome?
       Jist bundle up the gellie and be gone.
Chorus: *Movin on, we're aye movin on. ... etc.*

I feel particularly privileged to have had the Stewarts of Blair as part of my circle of friends over the past thirty years. This sad song was written for the late Alec Stewart and recalls a day when I was visiting him and his wife Belle. By that time, he was suffering terribly from leukaemia and was unable to play his beloved pipes any longer. Along with us in the front room at the cottage in Rattray were several members of his family, all of whom were pipers, and they were all discussing pipes tunes and trying them out. The look on old Alec's face just broke my heart.

❊ ❊ ❊ ❊ ❊ ❊ ❊ ❊ ❊ ❊ ❊

The Old Piper

He sat by the in-gle, so worn and so grey, And he
thocht o the pipes he no lon-ger could play. His
plaid and his tar-tan that once were his pride. His——
bon-net and brogues they are aa laid a-side.

2. He once walked so proudly to keep up his name,
   A son of Jock Stewart, a piper o fame.
   Through Scotland and Ireland he travelled afar,
   And when the guns thundered, he marched to the war.

3. In summertime often in rain, sun or snow,
   He piped for his living in the Pass of Glencoe,
   Or up by Loch Lochy where the mountains tower high,
   His music would skirl out for those passing by.

4. Noo he can't hold the chanter, his lips canna blaw
   Miss Proud and Loch Duich are faded awa.
   His feet canna tak him to the clear mountain streams,
   But I ken he hears pipin in the glen o his dreams.

Miss Proud and *Loch Duich* were two of Alec's favourite pipe tunes, and it was his dying wish that the latter mentioned be played at his funeral.

This song was written about a man I saw in a London pub, when I was down there attending a conference on folk music in the early 1980s. I was told he was a street musician, and his sad empty eyes and his Glasgow accent made me curious about who he was and what experiences had brought him to the situation he was trapped in. This was before the days when the scandal of Cardboard City became a national issue in the media.

✵ ✵ ✵ ✵ ✵ ✵ ✵ ✵ ✵ ✵ ✵

The Busker

Bo-ny fin-gers—— pick-ing a twelve string,—— Sad fun-ny clown face an

down at heel shoes; Un-sha-ven chin—— an teeth aa dis - co-loured,——

Chorus

Bus-king the thea——tre queues. Sing-ing,—— sing-ing the blues.

2. Wrapped up in his shabby overcoat,
    Not just the company you might choose,
    Sits in the pub, sipping the music,
    With plenty of worries to lose,
Chorus: *Singing, singing the blues.*

36

3. Glasgow accent, soft an throaty,
   A singing voice that's roughened with booze,
   His past is a mystery, his future in question,
   An there are not many clues,
Chorus: *Why he's singing, singing the blues.*

4. Drawn on his face is a map of memory,
   Hard times, hard roads that batter an bruise.
   Sunken eyes that wistfully wonder
   Why he never gets any good news,
Chorus: *Singing, sing the blues.*

The mining communities of Wales are no strangers to living with tragedy, since mining and danger to life go hand in hand with each other. However, the disaster at Aberfan in October 1966 taught us that even when the coal has been exhumed, there are hidden dangers in the bings of slurry that mining leaves behind. I came home from the school where I was teaching to see the tragedy at Aberfan reported on the television news, and the song virtually wrote itself. Welsh singer, Siwsann George did me the honour of translating it into Welsh and recording it on a Mabsant LP a number of years ago, and in July 1996, we sang both versions at the International Ballad Conference in Swansea.

✳ ✳ ✳ ✳ ✳ ✳ ✳ ✳ ✳ ✳ ✳

Aberfan

With Melancholy

A great tip of slur-ry hung a-bove the town And trucks from the coal pits kept add-ing to its crown. Then sud-den-ly one mor-ning, it all came roa-ring down, The day the moun-tain fell on A-ber-fan.

2. It carried off a farmhouse that clung to the hillside,
   It buried sixteen houses in its dark and deadly tide,
   And many were the families who disappeared or died,
   The day the mountain fell on Aberfan.

3. But that was not the end of the sorrow and the pain,
    For down upon the school poured the slurry's dreadful rain.
    And many were the children who would never laugh again,
    The day the mountain fell on Aberfan.

4. Their fathers fought barehanded to dig their children free,
    But all they found were broken limbs and eyes that could not see.
    And all the world lamented that this should ever be,
    The day the mountain fell on Aberfan.

5. There's mourning in the valleys that's terrible and new,
    They curse the men in power for the things they didn't do.
    And if you had been with them, would you not have cursed them too,
    The day the mountain fell on Aberfan?

On the 13th of March 1996, another school was at the centre of a different sort of tragedy, although no less horrific for all that, when gunman Thomas Hamilton marched into Dunblane Primary School, and massacred sixteen pupils and their teacher. This song, written to the tune of *Young Jamie Foyers*, is a lament for the innocent victims who died which, hopefully, expresses adequately what nobody could say to comfort the bereaved families in the immediate aftermath. The original copy of this song was put into a simple picture frame and laid in Dunblane Cathedral at the Vigil which was held for the victims by my elder son, Colin, and is now on display in the Chapter House.

✳ ✳ ✳ ✳ ✳ ✳ ✳ ✳ ✳ ✳ ✳

The Flooers o Dunblane

Tenderly and with feeling

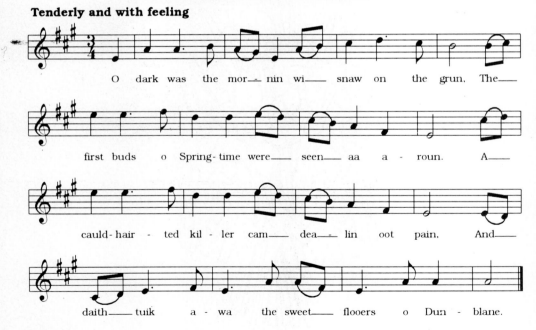

O dark was the mor—nin wi— snaw on the grun, The— first buds o Spring-time were— seen— aa a - roun. A— cauld-hair - ted kil - ler cam— dea—lin oot pain, And— daith— tuik a - wa the sweet— flooers o Dun - blane.

2. Oor sangs and oor fiddle tunes soun empty, the day,
   Oor feet winna dance and oor pipes winna play.
   Oor noontide is dark and oor tears faa like rain
   As we murn and lament the sweet flooers o Dunblane.

3. We aa hae kent sorrow and suffering and care,
   We aa hae lost dear yins that maks oor hairts sair.
   But we hope sic a dule will ne'er strike us again
   As we felt when we lost the sweet flooers o Dunblane.

In the late 1960s, my husband and I used to go regularly to Buckhaven Folk Club, where most of the members were miners or the family of miners who worked in the Michael Colliery. We heard about the fire underground just a short time before it went out of control. After the disaster, the colliery closed and many families had to move elsewhere. The following New Year when they came back for a reunion at the Folk Club, I was asked to sing this song : an unforgettable experience which convinced me once and for all of the value of folk song.

✱ ✱ ✱ ✱ ✱ ✱ ✱ ✱ ✱ ✱ ✱

Michael Colliery

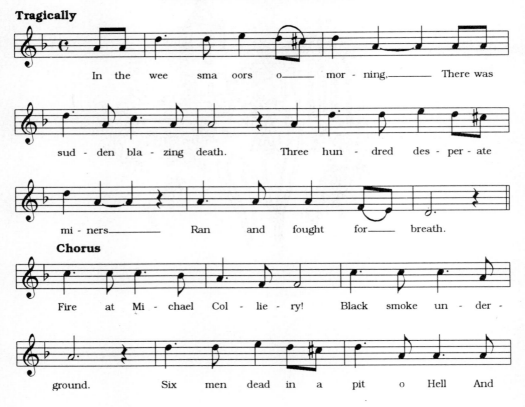

three   who   were   not————   found.

2. A mile below the pithead,
   Jock McArthur and his mate
   Were struggling through the darkness
   Tho they feared it was too late.
Chorus: *Fire at Michael Colliery,*
          Black smoke underground,
          Six men dead in a pit o Hell
          And three who were not found.

3. Jock knew the roads a lifetime,
   Found a place where air was clear.
   They banged upon the rock and heard
   A rescue party near.
Chorus: *Fire at Michael Colliery, ... etc.*

4. Down in the burning coalroads,
   Husbands and fathers died:
   The firemen could not master
   The raging flames inside.
Chorus: *Fire at Michael Colliery, ... etc.*

5. Dark was the billowing smoke cloud
   Hanging o'er Shaft Number Two,
   But darker the miners' future
   If there's no more work to do.
Chorus: *Fire at Michael Colliery, ... etc.*

When we move to a new home in another town, or even another country, we often feel like we do not fit in and wish we were back in familiar surroundings and with old friends. In this song, I tried to find images that express the feeling of loneliness and alienation we all experience at times throughout our lives.

✳ ✳ ✳ ✳ ✳ ✳ ✳ ✳ ✳ ✳ ✳

Lonely Things

The cry of the cur-lew on the high win-dy moor, The nest of the ea - gle and the wild ot - ter's spoor. These are all lone - ly things, lone - ly as I. They'll not hear the sound of my feet pas - sing by.

2. I'll walk owre the dark hills to the place that I know
   Where the wind sings a sad song to the trees bending low.
   These are all lonely places, lonely as I,
   They'll not hear the sound of my feet passing by.

3. The star in the heavens that's furthest away,
   The easternmost hilltop that sees break o day:
   These are all lonely things, lonely as I,
   If I follow the swallow, I'll soon learn to fly.

3. Comedy and Satire

This song won the Edinburgh Folk Club's first songwriting competition in the 1970s. It uses the traditional question and answer form, but the mother's advice to her daughter has been updated in the light of today's tolerance of greater sexual freedom.

❋ ❋ ❋ ❋ ❋ ❋ ❋ ❋ ❋ ❋ ❋ ❋

O Mither, Mither

O mi - ther, mi - ther, _____ what can a las - sie dae If I'm coor - tit by a fid - dler in the mer - ry month o May? _____ He'll touch me wi his bow _____ an mak my strings tae play. An I'm feart I may rue it in the mor - nin, O.

2. "O lassie, lassie, ye'll need tae learn the tune
O a slow air in April tae dance a jig in June,
An if ye pay attention tae the manage o yer goun
Ye'll never hae tae rue it in the mornin O."

48

3. "O mither, mither, whit can a lassie dae
   If he plays his penny whistle in the merry month o May?
   He has the finest fingers upon ma stops tae play,
   An I'm feart I may rue it in the mornin O!"

4. "O lassie, lassie, ye'll need tae learn the air,
   An then ye will discover that to dance a reel is rare.
   Jist place yer steps aright an ye never need despair
   Nor fear ye may rue it in the mornin O!"

5. "O mither, mither, whit can a lassie dae
   If he plays his concertina in the merry month o May?
   Wi his reed sae strang an free, he'll squeeze tae mak me play
   An I'm feart I may rue it in the mornin O!"

6. "O lassie, lassie, ye'll need tae learn the keys,
   Then ye will discover it can put ye at yer ease,
   For it's the very box o tricks a bonnie lass tae please
   An never fear ye'll rue it in the mornin O!"

7. O mither, mither, whit can a lassie dae
   If I'm coortit by a piper in the merry month o May?
   He has a braw chanter an his bag is never dry
   An I'm feart I may rue it in the mornin O!"

8. "O lassie, lassie, when ye hear him play the ground,
   Ye'll learn the variations that mak the pibroch sound;
   Ye'll forget aboot ceol beag when ceol mor comes around,
   An never fear ye'll rue it in the mornin O!"

9. "O mither, mither, yer words are wise I ken,
   An I will ever mind them in dealin wi the men,
   An when they play their music, I'll dance baith but an ben,
   An never fear I'll rue it in the mornin O!"

This song was based on a true story told to me by a teaching colleague, who was a personal friend of the farmer in question. He actually lived near Crieff, but since that's not an easy name to work into a song lyric, I used Comrie instead. I once had to sing it at a Farmers' Ceilidh in Crieff, and they all plied me with whisky to encourage me to reveal the name of the farmer, but I had somehow forgotten it!

❄ ❄ ❄ ❄ ❄ ❄ ❄ ❄ ❄ ❄ ❄

The Comrie Bull

A fair-mer oot by Com-rie had a herd o sex-starved kye,____ So he went tae Perth mar-ket a ran-dy bull tae buy.____ Five hun-dred gui-neas____ he paid u-pon the nail For a sperm-tes-ted a-ni-mal they said wad ne-ver fail.

Chorus

Oh the roa-rin o the bull,____ the

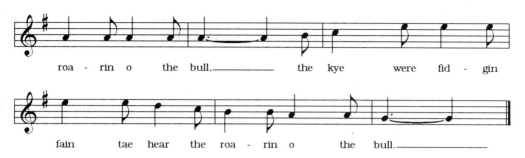

roa - rin o the bull,———— the kye were fid - gin

fain tae hear the roa - rin o the bull.————————

2. They took him hame fae market in a great big muckle truck,
   The fairmer thinkin aa the time o his maist unusual luck.
   As they rattled up the fairm road, the bull keeked oot on the sly
   An near went daft when aa he saw were fields an fields o kye.
   Chorus: O the roarin o the bull, the roarin o the bull,
   The kye were fidgin fain tae hear the roarin o the bull.

3. He rose early in the mornin his labours tae begin,
   The fairmer took him tae a field an led the heifer in.
   They circled roon each ither like moths aroon a flame,
   It didnae tak them lang tae learn that baith o them were game.
   Chorus: O the roarin o the bull, the roarin o the bull,
   He was rarin tae get goin was that randy roarin bull.

4. The fairmer jist tae help things on he held the heifer's heid,
   The bull cam tae't an very sune was workin up his speed.
   His lady love responded wi a passion sae intense,
   She backed intae him pushin him against an electric fence.
   Chorus: O the roarin o the bull, the roarin o the bull,
   O how excruciatin was the roarin o the bull.

5. The bull took aff across the fields jist like Apollo Seven,
   He went chargin up the hillside as if he was goin tae heaven.
   Aff he went across the muir, owre burn an dyke and rock:
   It took him twenty seiven oors tae recover fae the shock.
   Chorus: O the fleein o the bull, the fleein o the bull,
   It was jist like the Olympics tae see that fleein bull.

6. Noo when he sees a heifer he jist turns an rins a mile,
   The fairmer thinks o whit he cost an he cannae raise a smile,
   For a bull that winnae bull the kye is no sae greatly prized
   An the fairmer thinks he'll hae tae hae him psycho-analysed.
   Chorus: For he's a crazy mixed-up bull, a crazy mixed-up bull,
   He's conditioned against heifers, he's a crazy mixed-up bull.

The last decade or so has seen a strong trend towards keeping fit, running marathons and having a healthier diet. By means of a proliferation of magazines and programmes, we are all exhorted to do all kinds of things which are supposed to do us good, and in this mad quest for good health, we half kill ourselves. This song relies partly on it's visual effect.

✳ ✳ ✳ ✳ ✳ ✳ ✳ ✳ ✳ ✳ ✳

The Keep Fit Song

Jauntily

I love to go a-jog-ging—— a-long the coun-try roads, And get

splat-tered wi the lor-ries—— which just miss me wi their loads. My

feet are fu o blis-ters—— a-fore the day is done, But I

love to go a-jog-ging—— be-cause it is such fun!

2. I never miss my yoga, I go there twice a week
   And twist my legs and airms aboot until I'm feelin seik.
   I think I've got a hernia and my neck feels three parts screwed,
   But I never miss my yoga for it makes me feel sae good.

3. I'm really intae slimmin, I weight-watch aa the time,
   I eat nothin but Ryvita and drink soda water and lime.
   My stomach thinks my throat's cut and my social life is hell,
   But I'm really intae slimmin, for it makes me feel sae well.

52

4. Noo, the pleasure o aerobics is really hard tae beat,
    We jump aboot tae pop tunes till we paralyse oor feet.
    We go on for oors and oors for they winna let ye stop,
    But I really love aerobics because they buck me up.

5. The latest thing is health foods – great bowls o gritty grot,
    Weird salads and concoctions – I eat the haill damn lot!
    My taste buds are redundant and I'll never need a knife
    But I'll keep on with these health foods, for they'll transform my life.

6. But I think I've reached perfection wi a bike tae exercise,
    I pedal away for oors till the sweat runs in my eyes.
    I imagine that I'm cyclin fae Wick tae Elderslie,
    And the agony near kills me, so it must be good for me.

This song, written to a traditional tune, is my variation on *Seven Nights Drunk* and the night-visiting theme, where the man makes clandestine visits to his girlfriend's bed. The fellow in this song, however, doesn't come up to the mark. It merited a footnote in an article by Hamish Henderson in *The People's Past*, which was edited by Edward Cowan. It has been sung and recorded by other singers.

✳ ✳ ✳ ✳ ✳ ✳ ✳ ✳ ✳ ✳ ✳ ✳

On Monday Nicht

On Mon-day nicht he— cam tae my door An tir-led at the—
pin. "Rise up, rise up my— bon-nie lass And
let your lo - ver in." So— I rose up and
let him in and— on me he did faa. It was
five o'-clock in the mor - ning a - fore he gaed a - wa.

2. On Tuesday nicht he cam tae my door
   Again tae taste my charms.
   "Rise up, rise, my bonnie lass,
   And tak me in your arms!"
   So I rose up and let him in
   And wow, but he was fain –
   It was fower o'clock in the mornin
   Afore I lay my lane.

3. On Wednesday nicht he cam tae my door
   Jist a wee thing late in time.
   "I'd hae been here sooner, my bonnie lass,
   But the hill's owre hard tae climb!"
   He wasnae lang in my embrace
   Until he let me be,
   And he was oot the door again
   Afore the stroke o three.

4. On Thursday nicht he cam tae my door,
   Sair trachled in his gait.
   "O gie's a dram, my bonnie lass,
   And then, I swear, I'll dae't!"
   Aa nicht lang he focht wi it
   And I helpit him and aa,
   But only yince he managed it
   Afore the oor o twa.

5. On Friday nicht he cam tae my door,
   The joys o love tae share.
   "O cairry me in, my bonnie lass,
   For I can staun nae mair!"
   So I cairried him in tae my feather bed
   And his cheeks were pale and wan,
   And no an inch wad his hurdies rise
   Afore the oor o wan.

6. On Setterday nicht he cam tae my door;
   On hands and knees cam he.
   "O dinnae come oot, my bonnie lass,
   Stay in and let me be!"
   But I opened the door and I drew him in
   And he fell doon in a swoon,
   And oft tho I clasped him tae my breist,
   He lay like a log till noon!

One of the curses of Scotland is the insect known as "the mighty midge", which bites every part of the human body without mercy : anyone who walks, camps or even sits outside on a warm summer evening will testify to that. This song is my revenge – or maybe some of us might even consider it a tribute. The tune, of course, is *Bonnie Dundee*.

❋ ❋ ❋ ❋ ❋ ❋ ❋ ❋ ❋ ❋ ❋

The Midgie Song

Did ye hear o the set-tler wha cam tae the glen An bocht the laird's cas-tle for a wee but an ben; Pit in cen-tral hea-tin an pain-ted it braw, But he could-nae get rid o the mid-ges at aa.

Chorus

They bit aa his fin-gers, they bit aa his toes, They bit knees an el-bows, they bit ears an nose. They

bit eve - ry bit that the bligh - ters could bite, An they

kept up their bi - tin baith mor - nin an night.

2. He tried creams an lotions o every kind,
   He tried every remedy that he could find,
   But it never deterred them whene'er they zoomed in,
   Tho he even tried rubbin his hurdies wi gin.
   He scratched an he clawed an he clawed an he scratched
   Till pairts o his body were soon needin patched.
   The midges came back an they bit him some more
   An he clawed in some places he'd no clawed afore.

3. He blew smoke upon them an sprayed them wi turps,
   But that only led to a few farts an burps:
   He couldnae get sleepin because o the itch,
   So he tried oot a spell that he got fae a witch.
   He cursed them all but an he cursed them all ben:
   He cursed them the length an the breadth o the glen:
   He cursed them in Latin, Swahili an Dutch –
   But the midges spoke Gaelic an didnae care much!

4. When his posh freens cam northward tae fish an tae shoot,
   They'd hardly got started when they had tae scoot.
   The midges cam in, in their battle formations
   And the glen soon resounded wi loud exclamations!
   They ran thro the heather, they ran thro the gorse,
   The midges cam after them, out in full force:
   They ran roon in circles an in zig-zag lines
   An last seen were headin stracht doon the M9.

5. The settler went back tae his posh but an ben
   An sat doon an thocht whit he could dae then.
   As he doctored his midge bites wi a bottle o malt,
   He lamented his fate, felt it wasnae his fault.
   But he up sticks an left on the very next train
   An swore he'd no come tae the Hielans again,
   But the midges were mournin all thro the pinewoods,
   For they'd voted the settler their favourite food.

6. So it's no more forever noo doon in the glen,
   For strange are the ways o midges an men.
   They set off in dozens stracht doon the M1
   Tae seek oot that settler wha'd gien them such fun.
   They socht him in Yorkshire, they socht him in Kent,
   They asked aa the bees an wasps which way he went –
   One day he'll wake up all bitten an sore
   An he'll never get rid o those midges no more.

When they introduced the dreaded yellow no-parking lines to the streets of Perth, the list of the first batch of people caught out read like a Who's Who of the area. My husband Andrew was in very distinguished company! It was the two policemen coming to the house that inspired this song. The tune is *Dick Darby*.

✳ ✳ ✳ ✳ ✳ ✳ ✳ ✳ ✳ ✳ ✳

The Parking Song

Now you've all heard a-bout the train rob-bers——— Who stole ma-ny thou-sands of pounds,——— Or the men who ran off with the bul-lion——— by day-light in old Lon-don town.

2. Well, I've got them all beaten hollow,
   I've committed the worst crime on Earth,
   I'm the fellow who parked his old Hillman
   On the wrong side of Scott Street in Perth.

3. I left it for full fifteen minutes,
   Just as brazen and bold as you like.
   When I came back, two brave traffic wardens
   Were standing there ready to strike.

4. There's a wee notice up on the lamp post
   Which, sat at the wheel you can't spy.
   It's a hell of a life for the motorist,
   So don't stop here, drive right on by.

5. When the police heard of my misdemeanour,
   They acted with great diligence.
   Two uniformed men in a car came
   To charge me with this black offence.

6. The neighbours keeked out of their windows;
   They thocht I had murdered my wife,
   But little they knew – it was much worse,
   I'd be lucky to get off with my life!

7. In due course, I got a wee summons
   To appear on the 4th of September.
   But when I got there, oh! what a surprise:
   A bailie was the first offender.

8. So if you come to the Fair City
   In Volkswagen or Chevrolet,
   Be careful when you see those yellow lines
   And read what the notices say.

9. They don't care if you've shot your grandmother,
   Or embezzled a million or two,
   But if you're caught wrongfully parking,
   You've sure got it coming to you!

Glasgow in the 1960s had an unenviable reputation for gangland warfare and this song was prompted by an attempt by the pop singer, Frankie Vaughan, to get the Glasgow hard men to hand over their razors and bicycle chains during a so-called "amnesty" period. Knowing the Glasgow sense of humour as I did, I imagined the sort of response this publicity stunt might have among the small fry of the local underworld. The tune is *Galway Bay*.

✳ ✳ ✳ ✳ ✳ ✳ ✳ ✳ ✳ ✳ ✳

Glasgow Gang Song

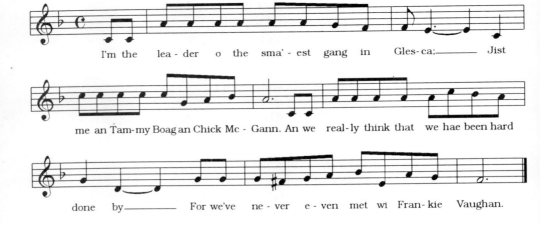

I'm the lea-der o the sma'-est gang in Gles-ca;———— Jist me an Tam-my Boag an Chick Mc-Gann. An we real-ly think that we hae been hard done by———— For we've ne-ver e-ven met wi Fran-kie Vaughan.

2. We heard aboot the amnesty for weapons,
   So we haunit in oor chivs an knives an junk,
   But the sergeant at oor local polis station
   Threw them back at us an said, "Noo, dae a bunk!"

3. He said they were the auld yins we'd nae yiss for:
   Tae haun them in wis jist a bluidy farce.
   For spilin oor grand gesture, said wee Tammy,
   We'd gie him yin o oor new yins up his – tunic!

4. We're really daein oor best tae be richt wi it,
   We havenae had a fight for owre a week.
   But naeb'dy's pit oor picters in the papers:
   We think it's jist a bit o bluidy cheek.

5. We're efter yin o thae community centres,
   Whaur we can hae a punch-up every nicht.
   We'll invite alang the haill o the Glesca Cooncil
   An pinch their wallets wance we've got them ticht.

6. Oh it's hard tae be the sma'est gang in Glesca,
   Ye get nae justice nae maitter whit ye dae.
   I think I'll jist awa tae jine the polis,
   The only gang in Glesca that draws pay.

An item in our local paper, The Perthshire Advertiser, inspired this song. The place in question was actually Lochearnhead, where the local part-time fire brigade was composed of men whose jobs made it hard for them to take immediate action in an emergency. The result of this was that when there was a fire, the Perth brigade got there first, so it was decided to disband the local one.

✳ ✳ ✳ ✳ ✳ ✳ ✳ ✳ ✳ ✳ ✳ ✳

The Auchentoshan Fire Brigade

Let's drink a toast tae that gal-lant band Wha's fame is kent owre aa the land. They're brave an bold an un-a-fraid. The

Chorus

Au - chen - to - shan Fire Bri - gade. To - shan, to-shan, Au - chen - to- shan, Au - chen - to- shan, to- shan O._____

2. Matt the shepherd is the Chief,
   Altho he's gettin unco deif.
   An when he's oot upon the hill
   He never hears the warnin bell
Chorus: Toshan, toshan, Auchentoshan,
   Auchentoshan, toshan O.

3. Rab the gamie, four foot ten,
   He really is the best o men.
   He walks aboot ten miles a day;
   When there's a fire, he's far away.
Chorus: *Toshan, toshan, Auchentoshan, ... etc.*

4. Jock the postie, sixteen stone,
   That's no exactly skin an bone!
   At fire-fightin he'll no fail
   Unless he's oot deliverin mail.
Chorus: *Toshan, toshan, Auchentoshan, ... etc.*

5. Jimmy Broon's the garage mech,
   He's serviced mony a battered wreck.
   But when the fire bell rings from afar
   He's sure to be beneath a car.
Chorus: *Toshan, toshan, Auchentoshan, ... etc.*

6. Willie Blyth keeps the hotel;
   In the tourist season he does well.
   At fire-fightin he is prime
   As lang's it's efter closin time.
Chorus: *Toshan. toshan, Auchentoshan, ... etc.*

7. Tam the jiner is the man
   Wha'll help in ony way he can.
   He'll sclim the ladder an no flegg
   If it wisnae for his widden leg.
Chorus: *Toshan, toshan, Auchentoshan, ... etc.*

8. So toast wi me this gallant band
   Wha's fame is kent owre aa the land.
   But if fire should break oot in your hame,
   Remember no tae coont on them!
Chorus: *Toshan, toshan, Auchentoshan, ... etc.*

This song is also based on an item in the local newspaper, and was written for children, and some of the local schools have taken it up quite enthusiastically. Of course, I've added a few more twists to the story to make it more outrageous. The song was included in my songbook for schools, called *Sing a Sing of Scotland*, published by Nelson in 1982.

❋ ❋ ❋ ❋ ❋ ❋ ❋ ❋ ❋ ❋ ❋ ❋

The Perth Pig

Chorus

Did you hear peo-ple say how the pig got a-way In the ci-ty of Perth on a cold win-ter's day? He ran and he jumped in the broad Ri-ver Tay, De-ter-mined to save his ba-con.

2. The pig he ran up and the pig he ran down,
   He ran along South Street and all round the town.
   He went to McEwen's without buying a gown,
   And to Christie's to see what was baking.

Chorus: *Did you hear people say how the pig got away*
In the city of Perth on a cold winter's day?
He ran and he jumped in the broad River Tay
Determined to save his bacon.

3. He approached Moncrieffe Isle with a wide piggy smile
    And made a bold fisherman run for a mile.
    He thought that the pig was some fearsome reptile
    And the pig didn't say he was mistaken.
Chorus: *Did you hear people say how the pig got away ... etc.*

4. Then up Kinnoull Hill he ran with a will;
    His murderous pursuers were after him still,
    And a pair in the long grass lying so still
    Had their sweet dream of love rudely shaken.
Chorus: *Did you hear people say how the pig got away ... etc.*

5. So the pig doubled back on his wild headlong track;
    Behind him, his hunters were still at his back,
    And down Lochy Brae he rolled like a sack
    But the folk at Brigend couldn't take him.
Chorus: *Did you hear people say how the pig got away ... etc.*

6. The pig was next seen on Gannochy Green,
    Dancing a jig, singing God Save the Queen.
    He was the happiest pig ever seen;
    He thought he had saved his bacon.
Chorus: *Did you hear people say how the pig got away ... etc.*

7. But to celebrate, it was a mistake;
    His hunters came up at a very fast rate,
    And down by the Tay, he met with his fate
    And the Perth pig became Perth bacon!
Chorus: *Did you hear people say how the pig got away ... etc.*

The late Hamish Imlach was a legend on the Scottish folkscene and could have been the perfect candidate to sing my *Keep Fit Song*, because he partook of all life's vices with a will and was totally unashamed of it. Always a man for a joke, he not only forgave me, but also appreciated this song. It was written to the tune of *Roddie McCorley* in the early 1970s after hearing a true story of what befell Hamish on Loch Lomondside. The reference to Hairy Mary in the last verse denotes a Glasgow song Hamish sang. "Hairy" is a Glasgow term for a working girl (who wore no hat).

✳ ✳ ✳ ✳ ✳ ✳ ✳ ✳ ✳ ✳ ✳ ✳

Hamish's Troosers

It was doon u—pon Loch— Lo - mond - side when the
moon shone bricht an clear, There— cam a wild folk— sing-in crew wi guitars an crates o beer Tae— camp u - pon the— is - land shore an—
sing the nicht a - way. But di - sas - ter— struck doon—
wan o them be - fore the dawn o day.

66

2. Noo, Hamish is a sonsy lad an a lad that loves a joke,
   He fell intae the watery loch an he got a richt guid soak.
   They fished him oot like a stranded whale, tho he'd scarcely breath tae blow
   An they hung his troosers up tae dry above the campfire's glow.

3. Draped in a blanket, Hamish sat an strummed his auld guitar,
   While his troosers steamed upon the shore by the licht o mune an star.
   In the wee smaa oors, someone awoke an "It's helluva cauld!" was the cry,
   An some hand threw petrol on the fire an sent flames roarin high.

4. Away with a whoosh went Hamish's breeks leavin never a trace behind:
   An anither pair o equal girth, well, nowhere could he find.
   Pity puir Hamish in his plight, nae troosers tae his name –
   They aa thocht he was Hairy Mary as he went toddlin hame.

There are literally hundreds of songs about "nice young girls" being led astray by lusty young suitors and being caught in a quandary about what to do when they are left in the lurch, dating from times when it was not considered proper for them to indulge in sexual activity until they were safely married. This song is just a bit of tongue-in-cheek fun-poking at tradition, from the perspective of today's atmosphere of greater sexual freedom.

✳ ✳ ✳ ✳ ✳ ✳ ✳ ✳ ✳ ✳ ✳

The Maiden's Lament

There's mo-ny a sang that be-gins wi the plea, Come aa ye young mai-dens tak war-nin fae me. An there is-nae o-ny sort o man as ye'll find No held tae be dan-ger-ous tae aa wo-man kind. So whit is a puir girl tae dae then? Whit is a puir girl tae dae? So-gers an sai-lors will love me an leave me. Tin-kers an tai-lors will cruel-ly de-ceive me. Whaur will I find a man

wha'll ne - ver grieve me? O—— whit is a puir girl tae dae?——

2. I've searched high an low for a young maiden's sang
   That disnae allude tae her sufferin wrang.
   An it seems quite unheard o for a girl tae hae fun
   Withoot losin her thyme, or mair crudely, bein done.
   So whit's a puir girl tae dae, then?
   Whit is a puir girl tae dae?
   Millers an troopers will only seduce me;
   Butchers an fairmers will slyly induce me
   Tae lower my standards, then ill they will use me –
   O whit is a puir girl tae dae?

3. Shairly it can't be the truth that they're singin,
   "Aa men are deceivers," tearin hair an haun wringin?
   I jist can't believe that the warld disnae hold
   A man wha will value me higher than gold.
   But whit is a puir girl tae dae, then?
   Whit is a puir girl tae dae?
   Fishermen sail far awa owre the ocean;
   Fiddlers arenae noted for their devotion;
   Earls hae been known tae slip ye a potion,
   So whit is a puir girl tae dae?

4. I sometimes reflect wi unmaidenly gall,
   My mind's no in truth wi these singers at all,
   For gin I heed their sangs then I'll wait till infinity
   Afore I will manage tae lose my virginity.
   But whit is a puir girl tae dae, then?
   Whit is a puir girl tae dae?
   Aa those puir fallen heroines wha seek tae divert you
   Fae polismen an grocers that threaten your virtue,
   Why is it they never ken why men desert you,
   So a puir girl wad ken whit tae dae?

It seems absolutely incredible to me how our beloved government continually pontificates about the Westminster Parliament as being the Mother of Parliaments, and that it believes in democracy for every other country in the world – all except Scotland, of course. This song was written in the aftermath of the 1992 General Election result, when the Scottish nation was once again frustrated in its desire for home rule.

✳ ✳ ✳ ✳ ✳ ✳ ✳ ✳ ✳ ✳ ✳ ✳

It's Not For The Scots

2. Freedom's for the Falkland Isles, Kuwait and Southern Africa,
   Romania, Czechoslovakia and far-off Nicaragua.
   But if we seek it, we are told it's foolish and half-cracked we are;
   It's not for the Scots! Not for the Scots!

Chorus: *Not for the Scots! Not for the Scots!*
Why is it good for ither fowk and not for the Scots?

3. But what about the dole queues and young fowk begging for their bread?
   What about the cut-backs that surely kill our future dead?
   If we accept these things we're mad, for if the truth of it be said,
   They're not for the Scots! Not for the Scots!

Chorus: *Not for the Scots! Not for the Scots!*
They're not good for ither fowk, so why for the Scots?

4. So let us pray that come it may that Scotland will her choice attain,
   Not with bombs and bullets, but with a claim of right that's plain.
   By the power of the people, we'll never let them say again,
   It's not for the Scots! Not for the Scots!

Chorus: *Not for the Scots! Not for the Scots!*
Why is it good for ither fowk and not for the Scots?

The Vietnam War is stamped on the consciousness of all Americans, especially those from the generation who were drafted and sent out there to fight. Many of them who came back were not as gung-ho about their experiences as a certain American airman was during a press interview conducted directly after he had returned from a mission over enemy territory. This song literally wrote itself : it didn't seem necessary to add any comment to what he actually said.

✳ ✳ ✳ ✳ ✳ ✳ ✳ ✳ ✳ ✳ ✳

The Vietnam Pilot

I'm not a war mon - ger at all. _____ I
just like hav - ing a ball. _____ Fly - ing
o - ver the beach to bomb the V C. It's
bet - ter than hav - ing sex or L S D.

2. This is a gentleman's war,
    We know what we're fighting for.
    We have nice white-capped stewards to hand us our sweets,
    And every night we sleep between sheets.

72

3. I want this war to be won,
   But meantime, I'm having some fun
   I'd like to start at the old DMZ
   And move northward bombing all that I can see.

4. Don't tell me civilians die,
   For straightway I'll give you the lie.
   There ain't no such thing as civilians there:
   They're teaching young kids to fire up in the air.

5. Now I'm flying every day.
   Through the heaviest ever triple A.
   I push the pickle and watch the bomb drop
   And I can't really see how it's all going to stop.

6. It's a thought that makes some people sick,
   But it gives me a thrill and a kick.
   That's why they hate me up there in Hanoi –
   A healthy, clean-living all-American boy!

One of the most infamous pieces of legislation the Tories introduced when Mrs Thatcher was Prime Minister was the Poll Tax. Everyone loathed it and did their level best to cause as much bother for its collectors as possible. This song was written as a joke for a friend of mine whose London flat was in a rather inaccessible corner. It is also a tribute to the millions of ordinary people who, in the end, brought it down and forced its repeal.

✳ ✳ ✳ ✳ ✳ ✳ ✳ ✳ ✳ ✳ ✳ ✳

The Poll Tax Dodger

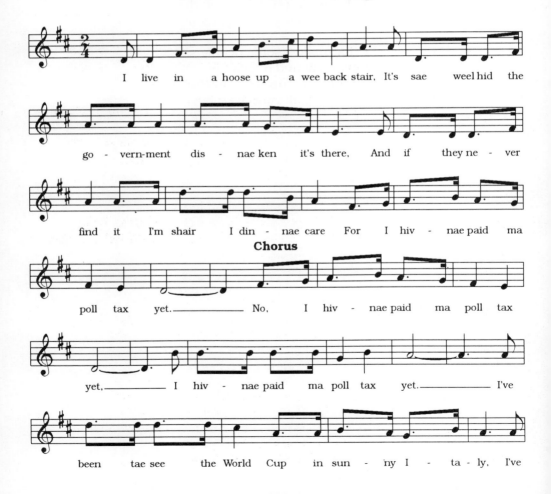

I live in a hoose up a wee back stair, It's sae weel hid the go - vern-ment dis - nae ken it's there, And if they ne - ver find it I'm shair I din - nae care For I hiv - nae paid ma poll tax yet.

Chorus

No, I hiv - nae paid ma poll tax yet, I hiv - nae paid ma poll tax yet. I've been tae see the World Cup in sun - ny I - ta - ly, I've

flown a-wa tae Thai-land tae hae a richt guid spree, I've

e - ven been tae toon a Run - rig con - cert for tae

see, But I hiv - nae paid ma poll tax yet.

2. Oh the stair is tirly whirly and there's shadows on the waa,
   And when ye turn the corner, ye canna see at aa.
   And naebody thinks onybody's livin there at aa,
   And I havenae paid ma poll tax yet.
Chorus: *No, I havenae paid ma poll tax yet, I havenae paid ma poll tax yet.*
   I've been tae see the World Cup in sunny Italy,
   I've flown awa tae Thailand tae hae a richt guid spree,
   I've even been tae toon a Runrig concert for tae see
   But I havenae paid ma poll tax yet.

3. I've had aa the reminders pit thro ma letter box,
   And I've been expectin someone comin rattlin at ma locks.
   But it seems as if I've gone tae earth jist like auld Renard Fox
   And I havenae paid ma poll tax yet.
Chorus: *No, I havenae paid ma poll tax yet, ... etc.*

4. Now I could buy a Porsche or a villa oot in Spain,
   A wardrobe o designer claes, or a mansion in Park Lane,
   Or a rock music studio tae bring me wealth an fame,
   But I havenae paid ma poll tax yet.
Chorus: *No, I havenae paid ma poll tax yet, ... etc.*

5. Noo, in maist o life's adventures, ma conscience is ma guide,
   In bein stracht an honest, I always tak a pride.
   But noo we've got a government that cheats on ilka side,
   So I havenae paid ma poll tax yet.
Chorus: *No, I havenae paid ma poll tax yet, ... etc.*

When I first went over to Ireland about fifteen years ago, it was with my husband and my elder son Colin, and for the last three days of our stay, we enjoyed the warm hospitality to be found in and around Milltown Malbay on the west coast of Clare. It is there we were introduced to poteen, a fine clear liquid about which there are many tales. This song incorporates two or three of them, including our own first experience. The name of the generous host has been changed to protect the innocent. The tune is that of a traditional Scottish song called *The Merchant's Son*.

❋ ❋ ❋ ❋ ❋ ❋ ❋ ❋ ❋ ❋ ❋

The Poteen Song

O have you been to the Coun - ty Clare And have you tas - ted the po-teen there? It's sweet as ho - ney and soft as dew With a kick like a kan - ga - roo. **Chorus** La - di- ri - fo - la, La - di - ri - fo- lay.

2. By Milltown Malbay I chanced to stray
   And found some lodging along the way.
   My host, Jack Wylie was far from mean
   To serve at breakfast time his good poteen.
Chorus: La di ri fo la, La di ri fo lay.

3. The taste delighted my palate so,
   The world took on a fine rosy glow.
   To buy a bottle was my intent
   And so to fetch some, Jack Wylie went.
Chorus: La di ri fo la, La di ri fo lay.

76

4. It was his neighbour, or so he said,
   Who had this wondrous concoction made.
   The nearest house was a mile or six,
   Yet he was back in two speedy ticks!
Chorus: La di ri fo la, La di ri fo lay.

5. But then I thought upon a snag,
   If the Excisemen found it in my bag ...
   Said Jack Wylie, "The story tell,
   It's sainted water from a holy well".
Chorus: La di ri fo la, La di ri fo lay.

6. That was fine, but then came the thought,
   "What happens when they find it's not?"
   "Just hold your hands up and shout aloud,
   A blessèd miracle has come about!"
Chorus: La di ri fo la, La di ri fo lay.

7. Oh just a drop of the mighty stuff
   To floor strong men can be quite enough,
   As twenty scholars found to their cost,
   When going homeward their way they lost!
Chorus: La di ri fo la, La di ri fo lay.

8. For two of them fell into a ditch;
   Another three o'er a cliff did pitch;
   Some stuck on fences, some sank in bogs,
   While one was tracked down by sniffer dogs!
Chorus: La di ri fo la, La di ri fo lay.

9. To give a welcome to Dublin Mick,
   They sent two bottles up to him quick,
   But Liam took too big a sup before
   And carelessly knocked at the Garda's door.
Chorus: La di ri fo la, La di ri fo lay.

10. When Sergeant Nolan came down the stairs,
    Poor Liam started to say his prayers,
    Then he thought of a cunning ruse
    And said, "I'm taking Dublin Mick a goose!"
Chorus: La di ri fo la, La di ri fo lay.

11. So here's to poteen and here's to Clare,
    And to the man up the road out there.
    And may that goose keep on laying well,
    That's all the story I have to tell!

Chorus: *La di ri fo la, La di ri fo lay.*

4. Real Life and History

It has always been my belief that nuclear power is inherently dangerous and there are millions of other people like me who would prefer a more natural form of power generation to be adopted in this country. The people of the Ukraine would, I am sure, agree with me, having suffered the adverse effects of the nuclear industry's most unthinkable scenario – a nuclear melt-down. What the advocates of nuclear power don't seem to be able to grasp is that the fall-out does not recognise national boundaries and it can affect people thousands of miles away. This song was written the same week the disaster at Chernobyl occured, before the world's media had decided how to pronounce it correctly. It is not a political song; just one of compassion for those who suffered the consequences of the event.

✳ ✳ ✳ ✳ ✳ ✳ ✳ ✳ ✳ ✳ ✳

Chernobyl Lullaby

Gently

Cher - no - byl O Cher - no - byl, be - neath a black cloud ly - ing, Hoo

mo - ny o your bair - nies live; Hoo mo-ny o them are dy - ing?

Chorus

Hish - ye - ba my bon - nie bair - nie, Hish - ye - ba my mau - kin,

Hish - ye - ba my bon - nie bair - nie, Sleep an din - nae wau - ken.

2. Rumours run an whispers fly.
   Who can find the answer?
   A ring o silence lies aboot
   The ring o spreading cancer.
Chorus: *Hish-ye-ba, my bonnie bairnie,*
   Hish-ye-ba, my maukin.
   Hish-ye-ba, my bonnie bairnie,
   Sleep an dinnae wauken.

3. Smoolin yont the frontier lines,
   The silent unseen danger
   Reaches oot the hand o death
   Tae touch the far-off stranger.
Chorus: *Hish-ye-ba, my bonnie bairnie, ... etc.*

There are times throughout our life when present day hassles can lead us to look back in the past and indulge in memories of childhood, when life was more carefree and responsibility was the property of our parents. The song evokes memories from my childhood and holiday visits to Seamill, a small seaside town on the Clyde Coast.

❊ ❊ ❊ ❊ ❊ ❊ ❊ ❊ ❊ ❊ ❊

Long Ago

Waves that beat on my shore, Fill-ing——— my
ears with your roar, Do you re-mem - ber———
feet that trod your sand long a - go; When I was a
child with shells in my hand long a - go?———

Chorus

I can't re - call the child I used to be, I've changed with the
years as you plain - ly can see. But you're still the same so per-

haps   you will know   And re - mem - ber that child   long a - go.

2. Rocks that stand by the sea,
   Black in the tide running free,
   Do you remember when there lay upon your back long ago,
   A small sunburnt child, curious of the clinging wrack long ago?
Chorus: *I can't recall the child I used to be,*
   I've changed with the years as you plainly can see.
   But you're still the same, so perhaps you will know
   And remember that child long ago.

3. Hills that look o'er the bay,
   Purple above the white spray,
   Do you remember the laughter of my heart long ago,
   As I ran thro the world where I'd still to play my part long ago?
Chorus: *I can't recall the child I used to be, ... etc.*

The North Sea oil boom of the 1970s was the greatest economic event in Scotland since the Industrial Revolution and caused a massive upheaval in the way of life in the north-east of Scotland. As more and more oil reserves were discovered offshore, more and more of the young men were lured from the more traditional industries of farming and fishing by the offer of fat wage packets and went to earn a living on the oil rigs. This is one of several songs I wrote for a workshop *The Black Black Oil*, which was held by the late Arthur Argo at one of the Inverness Folk Festivals during the early years of the boom.

✳ ✳ ✳ ✳ ✳ ✳ ✳ ✳ ✳ ✳ ✳ ✳

Slavery Nae Mair

Ma fa - ther wis___ a far - mer on bon - nie De - ve - ron - side,___ He booed his back an toiled an swat un - til the day he died.___ But I'll gyang tae the ile - rigs an mak a for___ - tune there;___ I'll mak a hun___ - ner pun a wick, An

ni - ver hae———— a care.————

2. Ma faither wore the nicky tams an a bunnet tae his heid,
   He spent his life in slavery, his bairnies for tae feed.
   But I'll gyang tae the ile rigs an be a king o men,
   Ma wife an bairns will aa fare weel an niver want again.

3. Ma faither wis contentit wi the little he cuid get;
   An gin he wis alive, the day, he'd be a peer man yet.
   But I'll gyang tae the ile rigs tae cheenge ma destinie,
   The days are by fan men will slave fir a pittance o a fee.

4. Come aa ye Buchan fairm loons an listen tae ma sang;
   Niver fear tae lea the lan or on a rig tae gyang.
   The wark is hard but the pey is guid; ye'll niver want fir breid;
   Wi siller in yeir pooches, ye can aye haud up yeir heid.

Scotland's once proud mining industry which helped to fire the Industrial Revolution is now a paltry shadow of its former self, with only a handful of pits still running. The bitter miner's strike of the mid 1980s is still a powerful memory in many of the mining communities of the central belt. This is a song to lament not just the virtual disappearance of the mining industry in Scotland, but also the callous way its effects were handled by the government.

✳ ✳ ✳ ✳ ✳ ✳ ✳ ✳ ✳ ✳ ✳

Goodbye to the Coal

Sleep ma wee bair-nie, your dad-dy's a mi-ner, But soon he'll have nae-thin tae dae. They're clo - sing the pit and the last shift is **Chorus** owre, And they're tur - nin the wor - kers a - way. Good - bye tae the coal, Good - bye tae the shaft and the cage. Good - bye tae the lamp and the coal- pick,_____ And good - bye tae a li- vin_____ wage.

2. Your faither worked hard tae keep the pit open;
   That's something that can't be denied.
   Noo they've taken his job, they've taken his future,
   They've taken his skill and his pride.

Chorus: *Goodbye tae the coal,*
        Goodbye tae the shaft and the cage.
        Goodbye tae the lamp and the coal-pick,
        And goodbye tae a livin wage.

3. A curse on the men who've done doon the miners,
   May they never sleep soun in their bed!
   Wha'll give him a job, wha'll give him a future,
   And see that his children are fed?

Chorus: *Goodbye tae the coal, … etc.*

This song is about my father, John Patrick (1900 – 1990), his experiences of working on the Clyde and his thoughts and feelings about them. His working life was spent in the hot, sweaty environment of many a ship's engineroom. He finally retired in 1965 to the town of Dalry in his native Ayrshire, where he lived happily until his death from cancer in January 1990.

✳ ✳ ✳ ✳ ✳ ✳ ✳ ✳ ✳ ✳ ✳

The Clyde Trust Engineer

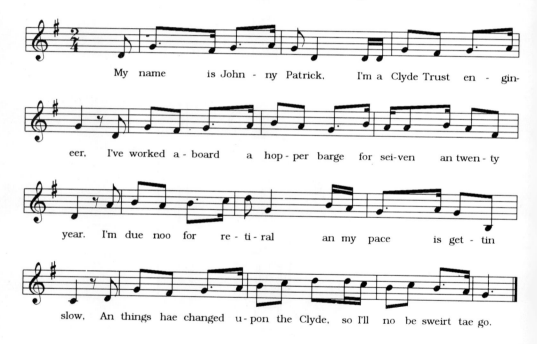

My name is John - ny Patrick, I'm a Clyde Trust en - gin-
eer, I've worked a - board a hop - per barge for sei - ven an twen - ty
year. I'm due noo for re - ti - ral an my pace is get - tin
slow, An things hae changed u - pon the Clyde, so I'll no be sweirt tae go.

2. When first I came tae Shieldhall Quay, the sirens filled the air;
   Tae keep the river open for the big ships wis oor care.
   I've seen the boat lying next us blown sky-high in the nicht,
   An I've seen the bombers owre the docks by the full moon's siller licht.

3. The firemen they tak on these days wad drive ye oot yer heid;
   They widnae ken a shovel fae a loaf o Bilsland's breid.
   Maist o the time they swing the lead, tell me tae go tae hell,
   So aften I hae tae buckle to an dae the job masel.

4. But noo there's mony changes an they're no aa for the guid;
   They're no sae easy tae accept when ye've engines in your bluid.
   They say that steam is gaun oot an it's diesel is the thing,
   But it's gey queer in the engine room wi the ither piston's ding.

5. But o aa the mony changes, I think it is maist queer
   That ye dinnae need a ticket noo tae be an engineer.
   I served ma time on ship wi names like Havildar and Sikh,
   Noo aa ye need's a boiler suit an a bit o brazen cheek.

6. Noo the Super is a man I hate – a man I cannae staun;
   He rules the men wi cunning an a mean an grudgin haun.
   Wan day he had an accident, it nearly made us seik,
   But the Weir's pump cuidnae brak his skull, it wis sae bluidy thick.

7. Tho things are gettin better an the work's no really bad,
   An we have the best conditions that we have ever had,
   I've kept ma watch an I've dune ma stint an cairried mony a load,
   Noo I'll sail yince mair tae the Garroch Heads, then it's I am for the road.

8. So ma name is Johnny Patrick, I'm a Clyde Trust engineer,
   I've worked aboard a hopper barge for seiven an twenty year.
   I'm due noo for retiral an ma pace is gettin slow,
   And things have changed upon the Clyde, so I'll no be sweirt tae go.

No one who was there will ever forget the tremendous excitement of the Blairgowrie Festivals run by the newly formed Traditional Music and Song Association in the 1960s. The tartan tomfoolery and mawkish kitsch peddled by television and tourist companies were cast aside, as the true authentic sound of Scottish tradition made itself heard – a cause for celebration indeed!

✳ ✳ ✳ ✳ ✳ ✳ ✳ ✳ ✳ ✳ ✳ ✳

The Blairgowrie Come-All-Ye

With Gusto

Come aa ye gen-tle peo-ple——— an hear whit I de-clare,——— I'll tell ye o a great e-vent gin ye hae time tae spare;——— Hoo fowk aa cam a-flo-ckin——— tae the Fes-ti-val o Blair,——— The sing-ers an mu-si-cians tae be heard by ane an aa.———

2. There were fiddlers an diddlers an men wha played the spoons;
    Ceilidh bands an pipers an pints for hauf a croon.
    An mony a bonnie singer wha kent the auldest tunes
    Aa cam tae Blairgowrie tae be heard by ane an aa.

3. There was Belle an Alec Stewart, the king an queen o Blair,
   Wi Sheila an Cathy tae sing aside them there.
   An the fiddlers fae Lochailort wi mony a liftin air
   Aa cam tae Blairgowrie tae be heard by ane an aa.

4. There was Willie Scott the shepherd an auld Jimmy McBeath:
   Beamin Daisy Chapman, wha's never short o breath,
   Tae sing o joy an sorrow an love an life an death,
   Aa cam tae Blairgowrie tae be heard by ane an aa.

5. Auld Davie Stewart wi his box an voice's ring:
   Couthy Mary Brooksbank wi Dundee sangs tae sing,
   An ballads fu o feelin we heard the Turriffs bring,
   Aa cam tae Blairgowrie tae be heard by ane an aa.

6. Across the sea fae Ireland cam freens we ken sae weel,
   Pat McNulty an the Fureys tae play us jig an reel.
   An Christy Moore the balladeer, a great reid-bearded chiel,
   Aa cam tae Blairgowrie tae be heard by ane an aa.

7. Forbye these weel-kent faces were ithers that were new,
   Some wi beards an hingin locks as wild as ever grew.
   Some wi guitars they cuidnae play, an that is strange but true,
   Aa cam tae Blairgowrie tae be heard by ane an aa.

8. Ithers there were instruments an voices fine tae hear:
   Aly Bain, Isla St Clair, a lintie sweet an clear.
   An mony ithers wham we hope tae meet again neist year,
   Aa cam tae Blairgowrie tae be heard by ane an aa.

For the benefit of those who don't know, I am proud to be a Scottish Nationalist and believe strongly that independence is the best future for Scotland. The last sixteen years of Conservative government from Westminster have only hardened that belief. But that does not mean that we have to hate our southern neighbours, or anyone else for that matter who decide to come and make their lives here. Having been born in Yorkshire and with a Yorkshire mother, I can hardly do that. However, we do need to cast off our ostrich mentality and start believing in ourselves as a nation again.

❊ ❊ ❊ ❊ ❊ ❊ ❊ ❊ ❊ ❊ ❊

The Day of Freedom

O when the great day o free-dom comes, We'll gie it a weel-cam wi pipes an wi drums, We'll live oot the dreams we hae longed tae ful-fil And we'll mak oor Scot-land grea—ter still.

2. Amang aa the nations we'll tak oor stand,
   Restored and reborn as a sovereign land.
   We'll carry the emblems from oor proud past,
   The shameful Union will be broken at last.

3. Oor people will walk wi their heids held high,
   And, "Onward for Scotland!" will be their cry.
   They'll work wi mair purpose when they ken they are free;
   We'll lose nae mair o them ayont the sea.

4. When oor statesmen hae pooer owre aa oor affairs,
   There'll be strachter dealins and fairer shares.
   The need of oor people will be understood,
   We winna be written aff as jist a backwood.

5. We'll feel a new spirit that strives tae create;
   New enterprises will prosper the State.
   New sangs and new writins, new thocht and new airt
   Will burst intae bloomin when we aa get new hairt.

6. Then lift up your voices and sing o your hope;
   Dinna let Blair or Major sell you any dope.
   The great day is comin : its dawn I can see,
   When Scotland will ken its auld libertie.

As I have already mentioned, the oil boom in the North Sea had a tremendous effect on the north-east of Scotland, where much of the youthful workforce deserted the traditonal industries of the area to go to the oil rigs. While it has been the case that the oil boom has been of benefit in economic terms, not everyone was pleased to see the arrival of so many outsiders, who will, no doubt, disappear again when the oil runs out. There were also concerns about pollution and the effect it would have on the local wildlife. This song was written for the songwriting competition at Thurso Folk Festival in the early 1970s, in which it gained first place. Since then, it has been sung and recorded by a number of singers, such as Arthur Johnstone and Andy Ramage, broadcast and used in a film and a stage show.

❊ ❊ ❊ ❊ ❊ ❊ ❊ ❊ ❊ ❊ ❊

The Men o the North

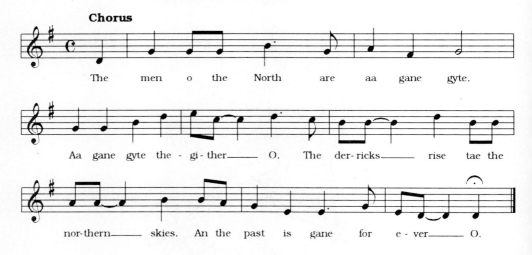

1. As I cam in by Peterheid,
   I saw it changin sairly O,
   For the tankers grey stand in the bay
   An the oil is flowin rarely O.

Chorus: *The men o the North are aa gane gyte.*
Aa gane gyte thegither O.
The derricks rise tae the northern skies
An the past is gane forever O.

2. The lads fae the Broch hae left the fairm;
   Aff tae the rigs they're rushin O,
   For ye get mair pay for an oilman's day
   So they heedna the ploo nor the fishin O.
Chorus: *The men o the North are aa gane gyte, ... etc.*

3. I met wi a man fae Aiberdeen;
   That city aye sae bonnie O.
   He said, "There's a spree by the dark North Sea
   An an affa smell o money O."
Chorus: *For the men o the North are aa gane gyte, ... etc.*

4. Whit wad ye gie for the gowden sand,
   The whaup's cry in the mornin O.
   The rowan fair an the caller air
   An the tide as it's gently turnin O?
Chorus: *But the men o the North are aa gane gyte, ... etc.*

With the coming of the Common Market and the European Union, there have never been any shortage of disputes of one kind or another. Fishing grounds have been one such area which has been hotly disputed between European Union partners. The inspiration for this song was a particular incident in the mid-1980s concerning a Danish fisherman, Captain Kent, who was caught breaching EC rules. Concern had been expressed about dwindling fish stocks in the North Sea and the threat to UK fishermen's livelihoods from foreign boats fishing in UK waters, so the government decided to impose a limit round the UK where only UK boats could fish. The absurdity of the idea in the song sums up for me the stupidity of bureaucracy, that thinks human problems can be solved by making rules. The tune is that of a popular children's song called *Coulter's Candy*.

✸ ✸ ✸ ✸ ✸ ✸ ✸ ✸ ✸ ✸ ✸ ✸

Lines Upon the Water

Chorus

How many fish are in the sea. No e-nough for you an me.

Verse

So they say there-'ll have to be Lines u-pon the wa - ter. Oor

fi-sher-men say it must be war.— Their live - li-hood they're figh-ting for. So they've

drawn a line twelve miles from the shore. Lines u-pon the wa - ter.

2. Captain Kent sailed owre the faem
   Tae catch a sprat far fae his hame,
   An prove by playin sic a game
   Ye can't draw lines on water.
Chorus: *How many fish are in the sea?*
   No enough for you an me,
   So they say there'll have tae be
   Lines upon the water.

3. The court has fined him thirty grand
   An say it is the law o the land,
   But Captain Kent jist waved his hand
   An said, "It's only money!"
Chorus: *How many fish are in the sea? ... etc.*

4. Wha is richt an wha is wrang?
   Wha's tae say the fish belang,
   Tae them or us? The weak an strang
   Are aye in disagreement.
Chorus: *How many fish are in the sea? ... etc.*

5. Fish cannae read an dinnae ken
   The unco ways o fishermen,
   An they have never seen the pen
   That draws lines on the water!
Chorus: *How many fish are in the sea? ... etc.*

As I have already mentioned, my father worked as an engineer on the Clyde Trust hopper barges : before that, he sailed all over the world to all sorts of exotic places. While he was away at sea, my mother returned to Yorkshire, where I was born, and I was three years old before I met my father for the first time. I wrote this song after hearing a beautiful song called *I Never Found My El Dorado* written by the English songwriter, Graham Miles. It struck me it that my father, who did go to sea, saw all the far away places and wonderful sights mentioned in the song. He also found his El Dorado – but not across the ocean.

✳ ✳ ✳ ✳ ✳ ✳ ✳ ✳ ✳ ✳ ✳

Not El Dorado

My fai-ther sailed the se-ven seas.___ An walked on mo-ny a fo-reign shore,___ Saw aa the won-ders o the world___ He'd on-ly dreamt a-bout be-fore.___

Chorus

He saw it aa. he saw it aa,___ He saw the subs-tance; not the sha-dow,___ But in his hairt o hairts he knew___ That nane o it wis El Do-ra-do.___

2. He walked through palaces of gold
   An gardens bricht wi fruit an flooer;
   Saw lovely islands in the sun
   Whaur he spent mony a happy oor.
Chorus: He saw it aa, he saw it aa,
   He saw the substance, not the shadow.
   But in his hairt o hairts he knew
   That nane o it wis El Dorado.

3. He told me tales o auld bazaars
   An jewelled treasures fair tae see;
   O monkey, elephant an snake,
   Lotus an palm an banyan tree.
Chorus: He saw it aa, he saw it aa, ... etc.

4. He luiked on monument an dome
   O marbled white an golden glory,
   O Shwe Dagon an Taj Mahal,
   Fabled in ancient sang an story.
Chorus: He saw it aa, he saw it aa, ... etc.

5. But when he anchored in the Clyde
   An yince again he walked ashore,
   The ties o hame had grown owre strang,
   He swore he'd gang tae sea no more.
Chorus: He'd seen it aa, he'd seen it aa;
   He'd seen the substance, not the shadow.
   An in his hairt o hairts he knew
   That hame's the only El Dorado.

In recent years, there have been a number of highly publicised disputes against the building of new roads such as those of the Newbury Bypass and the M77 extension, and the increasing encrochment of urban sprawl into the green belt. In many ways, although this song was written back in the early 1970s for a BBC Radio programme of songs on the theme of conservation, produced by the late Arthur Argo, it could be said to be of relevance today.

❇ ❇ ❇ ❇ ❇ ❇ ❇ ❇ ❇ ❇ ❇

Will There be a Green Place Left?

In the days o auld lang syne, A - fore the fac - to-ry hand or mi-ner, The banks o the Clyde were green an fair An fish swam in the Mo - len-di-nar. But time pas-ses, times change. So dae the things that men be-lieve in. Noo fish don't swim by the Broo-mie - law. They choke tae death on the banks o the Le-ven.

2. Long ago when the hills were young,
   The red deer fed on the forest floor.
   Wider then their antlers spread
   An prouder sounded their vaunting roar.
   Then came man with his sporting gun
   An drove the stag from the glens an forest,
   A hungry fugitive to the moors,
   The barren rocks an distant corries.

3. The restless bulldozers work on an on
   To build new towns an six-lane highways,
   An a million wild things have to flee
   An leave their haunts an leafy byways.
   Oh will there be a green place left
   For Man an all the rest of nature,
   Or will the tide of tarmac drown
   Them all, an leave no living creature?

In this song, I am preoccupied by the growing problems of pollution and the destruction of natural beauty. Once again, it has almost a prophetical quality to it, because although it was written some twenty years or more ago, it has a strong relevance today with the problem of global warming which is now becoming apparent. In our pursuit of material things, the great tide of scientific advance we have made has rendered us wasteful and blind to the fact that it is having a profoundly detrimental effect on our environment, and that unless we change our ways soon and become more environmentally friendly, our days could be numbered.

❊ ❊ ❊ ❊ ❊ ❊ ❊ ❊ ❊ ❊ ❊

The Quiet of the Glens

The wiz-ards of tech-no-lo-gy are gath-ered in their halls With plans to move the moun— tains and tame the wa-ter-falls. But when they've built their mo-tor-ways And their ci-ties rise im-mense, Will I know where to find a-gain the qui-et of the glens?

2. The wheels of progress turn and turn and never will run back,
   And the human race keeps struggling on to follow in their track.
   But things often seem to go too fast and cause a thousand ills,
   And we long again for greenery and the peace of lochs and hills.

3. O change for change's sake's no good, what's new's not always best
   If it robs the world of beauty; kills the soul within the breast.
   I find no comfort in machines nor the luxury of goods
   If I can never roam again the happy fields and woods.

4. The lap of river water falling softly on the ear,
   The silver flash of fishes where the water's running clear,
   The sight of far-off peaks the setting sun has touched with fire
   Are worth more than the scientific Land of Heart's Desire.

5. What nameless cancer is it that eats the human heart
   And makes Man so despoil the world of which he is a part?
   We pollute the air and water and mutilate the land,
   And yet we could prevent it all – it lies within our hand.

This song dates back to the Falklands War, when the Thatcher government decided, however belatedly, that the Falklanders were British after all and sent the Task Force south to liberate the islands. When war was declared, and while sitting watching television pictures of the ships leaving harbour laden with soldiers and military hardware, I couldn't believe that we were going through again what I'd had known in my childhood and thought was past and over. But I have come to realise that, with troops having been sent off to the Gulf and to Bosnia since then, this is a timeless song that keeps getting sung over and over again. The tune is *All Around my Hat.*

✳ ✳ ✳ ✳ ✳ ✳ ✳ ✳ ✳ ✳ ✳ ✳

The Soldier's Wife

2. When first he went aboard the great grey liner,
   The crowds were aa cheerin and the flags were wavin free.
   And when he stood on deck wi his kitbag aside him,
   I cuidnae see his smile for the tear in my ee.

3. The last ship disappeared o'er the distant horizon,
   And I went hame my lane tae feed my bairnies twa.
   The newspaper headlines were fu o dule and warnin
   In print black and stark as thon cursèd hoodie craw.

4. Then word came o battles in air and on water,
   Lives they were lost and fine ships they went doon.
   O wae wis I for them, but thocht it nae wonder,
   For gin ye cairry weapons, ye'll shairly yaise them soon.

5. So noo here I stand on the banks o the ocean,
   Wishing that the war and the fechtin will cease,
   And my love will come hame again tae see his bonnie bairnies
   And the stormy South Atlantic will become a sea o peace.

The coming of the North Sea oil bonanza in the 1970s didn't just mean employment for people working offshore on the rigs : the rigs themselves had to be built and so there was a demand for people to work in the fabrication yards at the likes of Nigg Bay on the Moray Firth. While the wages were high, it also meant that the men were away from their families for weeks and staying in somewhat objectionable accommodation and there was not much to do in the way of recreation, as this song points out. This is another of the several songs I wrote for the late Arthur Argo's *Black Black Oil* workshop held at one of the Inverness Festivals.

✳ ✳ ✳ ✳ ✳ ✳ ✳ ✳ ✳ ✳ ✳

The Fitter's Song

O I am a fit - ter, I work in Nigg Bay, Tae build the big ile rig I'm toi - ling by day. At nicht I get fu on the whis - ky and rum, Then I sleep on ship board un - til the day comes. **Chorus** Wi a too - ra - li - ad - dy, wi a too - ra - li - ay.

2. For a man wi nae faimily this life's aa richt,
   But a man far fae hame is gey lanely at nicht.
   For there's naethin tae dae here but labour and drink,
   And the quarters we live in's no fit for a tink.
Chorus: *Wi a toora-li-addy, wi a toora-li-ay.*

3. They say they'll build hooses for workers like me,
   But a story like that I'll believe when I see.
   For doon in the cities they cannae keep pace,
   So hoo will they dae it in this far-off place?
Chorus: *Wi a toora-li-addy, wi a toora-li-ay.*

4. The wages are high and the oors arena bad,
   In some ways the best job that I've ever had.
   But besides work and wages, there's mair tae this life,
   And I miss my three bairns and my bonnie bit wife.
Chorus: *Wi a toora-li-addy, wi a toora-li-ay.*

5. O there's work here a-plenty for months far ahead;
   There's hundreds o men that wad work in my stead.
   So I'll coont my blessins an nae stint in my toil
   Tae help build the rig that will bring hame the oil.
Chorus: *Wi a toora-li-addy, wi a toora-li-ay.*

This song commemorates the disaster that befell Willie and Bella MacPhee in January 1993, the year of the big flood in Perth, and tells of the struggle they had with the local Council to have their trailer replaced. The Council had towed seven of the caravans at the Doubledykes traveller's site into a neighbouring field while they were refurbishing the washblocks on the stances. That was why they sank in the mud when the floodwaters came through. Then they tried to tell those who had lost everything that they weren't Council tenants (inspite of the fact that they paid rent to the Council, who had built the site) and could not, therefore, be given compensation. In the end the Council relented and showed humanity towards the travellers.

❊ ❊ ❊ ❊ ❊ ❊ ❊ ❊ ❊ ❊ ❊

The Flood at Doubledykes

In the cru - el— month o Ja - nu-a - ry in the year o— nine- ty three,— 'Twas then a great mis - for—- tune be - fell— big Wil - lie Mac-Phee,— When the ra - ging Ri - ver Al—- mond burst thro— his trai - ler— door— And scat-tered his pos - ses - sions to be lost for— e - ver - more.—

2. It was out there at the Doubledykes whaur the traivellin people dwell,
   The storm that howled aboot that nicht no human tongue can tell.
   The caravan we'd ceilidhed in was cowpit on its side
   And thro the water and the mud for their lives they had to wade.

3. And when the nicht was over and the mornin came again,
    There were mony, mony hameless fowk tae be fun on Muirton's plain.
    The toun o Perth wad help them aa, it shairly cuidnae fail,
    But for the traivellin people – well, that was a different tale.

4. Tho claes an blankets they were given tae help them aa tae cope,
    O compensation for their vans they were telt they had nae hope.
    "You are not Council tenants, you just don't qualify!"
    That was the official answer and it shairly was a lie.

5. Wi letters tae the Cooncil, the MP and EEC,
    And a fechtin Brechin lawyer tae mak a legal plea,
    Wi the Press and television there tae bring it aa tae licht,
    Noo Willie and his freens hae won their basic human richt.

6. But oh, the hand o bureaucracy is a cauld unfeelin hand,
    Tae send a man o echty three scourin up and doon the land
    Tae find a trailer – cheap, of coorse, and o a modest length,
    The search has pushed big Willie tae the limit o his strength.

7. But noo a trailer has been foond and a new stairt can be made,
    And Willie can play his pipes again that miraculously were saved.
    The Cooncil that treats the traivellers as only seicont best,
    Noo kens the law supports them when it's put tae the test.

8. So here's to Willie and Bella MacPhee and aa their kith and kin!
    Lang may they live at Doubledykes, secure fae storm and wind.
    Wi thanks tae aa their mony freens wha saw justice win the day,
    And we'll have mony a ceilidh yet tae drive oor cares away.

affa	very, awful
agley	awry
ane an aa	one and all
ane	one
auld lang syne	the good old days
aye	always
bairn	child
baith	both
Bilsland's (breid)	a Glasgow bakery
blins	blinds
bocht	bought
booed	bowed
braw	fine, handsome
bricht	bright
brochan	oatmeal
buckle to	join in and help
burnie	stream
but an ben	2-roomed house/in and out
cairn	a heap of stones
canna	cannot
ceol beag	small music (of pipes)
ceol mor	big music (of pipes)
cheenge	change
chivs	razors
chuckles	pebbles
claes	clothes
coortit	courted, wooed
corries	mountain hollows
couldnae, cuidnae	could not
creels	baskets
croon	crown
cushie doo	wood pigeon
dabhaun	skilful person
deif	deaf
delichts	delights
dinnae	do not
dule	grief, sorrow
echty	eighty
fairmwark	farm work
fan	when (N.E. Scotland)
feart	afraid
fechtin	fighting
fey	other-worldly, supernatural
flegg	frighten, be frightened
forfochen	exhausted, out of breath
fowk	folk, people

fu	full, drunk
gaed awa	went away
gane gyte	gone mad
Garroch Heads	headlands at the mouth of the Clyde
gellie	traveller's tent
gey	very
ghaist	ghost
gied	gave
gien	gave, given
gin	if
gloamin	twilight
gowden	golden
grun	ground
guid	good
gyang	go (N.E. Scotland)
hae	have
haill	whole
hame	home
haunit	handed
hecht	promised
hish ye ba	hush a bye
hoodier crow	hooded crow, raven
hoose	house
houlet	owl
hurdies	hips, buttocks
ile	oil
ilka	every, each
ingle	hearth, fireside
jine	join
keeked	peeped
ken	know
kye	cattle
laigh	low
loons	boys
maukin	pitiful child
mavis	song thrush
micht	might
midges	small biting insects
muckle	big
murn	mourn
my lane	on my own
naethin	nothing
nane	none
nicht	night
nicky tams	knee-straps
oors	hours
owre	over, too

111

peer, puiur	poor
pleisure	pleasure
ploo	plough
poke	sack, bag
polis	police
pooches	pockets
powny	pony
pun	pound
rig	ridge, strip of ploughed land
schuilin	schooling
sclim	climb
seik	sick
shaddie	shodow
sic	such
siller	silver, money
simmer	summer
skirl	shrill out
smoolin	sneaking
snaw	snow
socht	sought
sonsy	buxom
spile	spoil
spilin	spoiling
staun	stand
stracht	straight
sweirt	reluctant
tatties	potatoes
telt	told
the Broch	Fraserburgh (colloquial)
thegither	together
timmer	timber
tirly-whirly	spiralling
trachled	exhausted
traivelt	travelled
tuik	took
unco	strange
wabster	weaver
wae	woeful
wance	once
warlock	wizard
weel-kent	well-known
whaup	curlew
widnae	would not
winna	will not
yince	once
yiss	use
yoke	cart
yont	beyont